THE CASE OF
THE PICKPOCKET ON SKIS

Dr. Bytes could not make a positive identification of the pickpocket.

One of the suspect skiers said that he couldn't have committed the crimes. The only place he ever skied—under the gondola—enabled him to practice slaloming in and out of the strong shadows cast by the gondolas. This is what he was doing on the day of the thefts.

Brent had his parka and was heading for the door.

"Where are you off to, son?" asked his father.

"The gondola slalomer is a liar. And I bet I'll be able to prove it."

How did Brent unmask the slippery ski-slope thief? Read on for the computerized solution!

Bantam Books in the Bytes Brothers Series
Ask your bookseller for the books you have missed

The Bytes Brothers
ENTER THE EVIDENCE

A Solve-It-Yourself Computer Mystery

Lois and Floyd McCoy

Illustrations by Leslie Morrill

BANTAM BOOKS

TORONTO • NEW YORK • LONDON • SYDNEY • AUCKLAND

RL 5, IL age 10 and up

THE BYTES BROTHERS ENTER THE EVIDENCE
A Bantam Book / October 1984

The Bytes Brothers is a trademark of Lois and Floyd McCoy

ISBN 0-553-24421-3

Published simultaneously in the United States and Canada

Bantam Books are published by Bantam Books, Inc. Its trademark, consisting of the words "Bantam Books" and the por-
trayal of a rooster, is Registered in U.S. Patent and Trademark
Office and in other countries. Marca Registrada. Bantam
Books, Inc., 666 Fifth Avenue, New York, New York 10103.

PRINTED IN THE UNITED STATES OF AMERICA

O   0 9 8 7 6 5 4 3 2 1

```
1000 REM DEDICATION
1010 PRINT "FOR HARRY RICH,"
1020 PRINT "A FAVORITE RELATIVE OF THE BYTES BOYS."
1030 END
```

The authors wish to thank Errol Weiss, Professor William E. Southern, Ph.D. (Department of Biological Sciences, Northern Illinois University), Naomi Katz, Steve Young (Instructor, Park City [Utah] Ski School), the Hon. Eve Preminger (Supreme Court of the State of New York), David Robinson, Dr. Jeffrey Weissel and Rose Ann Weissel (Lamont-Doherty Geological Observatory); and Carolyn Hughes for technical assistance. Marion Corkett's editorial expertise and Ted Enik's artistic flourishes are appreciated.

Contents

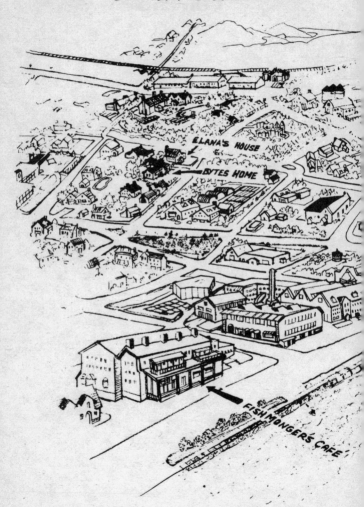

·❧ LAMONT LANDING ❧·
· THE BYTES BROTHERS' HOME TOWN ·

ELANA'S HOUSE

BYTES HOME

FISH MONGERS CAFE

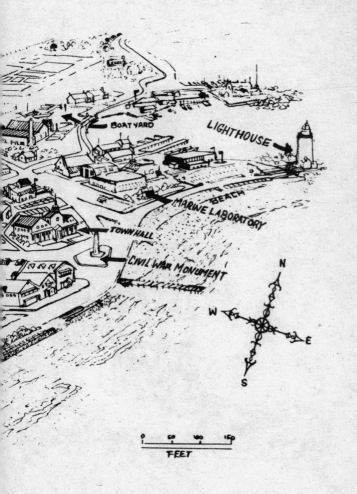

1

Obelisk

The sun was rising over the village of Lamont
Landing, and the crisp shadow of the Civil War
Monument stretched like an arrow toward Town
Hall.

Old Jeb Brown enjoyed the warmth of the April
morning as he lounged in his usual spot, against
the south side of the obelisk—a four-sided needle
of sandstone. A comfortable sea breeze brushed
his grizzled face. Jeb loved that cool southerly
wind.

At the sound of the sea gulls, Jeb opened his
eyes and squinted up at the sky. The birds flew
due south every day exactly at this time. Jeb always considered the birds' flight a signal to head
toward Town Hall for his usual cup of coffee with
Luke Gardner, the caretaker there.

Before he left, Jeb rubbed his fingers over the
writing on his side of the obelisk, as he did each
morning:

IN MEMORIAM

LT. JEB BROWN
The Battle of Gettysburg
1863

If it weren't for the strong morning shadows, he wouldn't be able to read the worn-away lettering at all. Jeb's satisfied expression became a frown. His chin burrowed into his chest as he walked to Town Hall for his coffee with Luke.

"Luke, my grandfather's name is disappearing from the memorial. I wouldn't be surprised if it was gone before I am. And that's not saying much, danged it all."

Luke looked understanding. "Listen, Jeb, ole' boy," he counseled, "stone can't help but wear away with time."

Jeb's face was stubborn. "It's more than that. My eyes aren't so great anymore, but my fingers are. And I can tell you, Luke, that that memorial to my grandfather has rotted away more in the past six months than it did in the last twenty years. And I know why." His eyes narrowed. "That boatyard and all the sandblasting they do, that's why."

Luke warmed to the subject. "And how 'bout that incinerator with smoke billowing out like crazy? Don't think that don't have an effect on things around here." He coughed for emphasis.

"And those new-fangled parking meters. Kids grow up, they won't know how to count with all these digital readouts. And not only that. . . ."

The community meeting was in full swing. Thirteen-year-old Barry Bytes and his eleven-year-old brother, Brent, trailed after their mother as she squeezed down the crowded aisle.

The mayor was speaking: The sandstone on the outside of the Town Hall building was rapidly deteriorating; no one was sure why.

He caught sight of the boys and their mother. The mayor had asked Dr. Bytes, a scientist, to attend. Her expert opinion might be useful.

"I see Dr. Bytes is here." He looked in her direction. "Perhaps you could shed some light on the problem?"

"Not so fast, Mayor." Jeb Brown's voice came from far in the left corner. "Before we start listening to the experts, maybe we'd better make sure we agree as to what's causing the problem."

"A little backward, if you ask me," commented Brent.

Smile lines creased alongside Dr. Bytes's eyes as she whispered in her younger son's ear: "Old Jeb doesn't want any facts interfering with his conclusions."

Jeb was continuing: "I know that Sam Dorey's boatyard is what's eating away our historic Town

Hall. And so does everyone else who's ever seen all that grit from his blasted sandblasting and watched the smoke coming out of his chimney. So before Dr. Bytes has her say"—he smiled politely toward her—"I think we should vote to close him down if he doesn't stop ruining our town."

"Holy macro." Barry shook his head. "That ole' Jeb is a walking syntax error if I've ever heard one."

Before the meeting ended, Dr. Bytes said a few words. So did Dr. Glassman, a scientist interested in the chemical makeup of rocks. The geochemist explained that, just like the Capitol Building in Washington, D.C., the Town Hall's facade, or outer shell, was made of a rock type called sandstone— tiny pieces of sand held together by a natural cement of calcium carbonate.

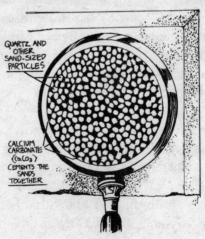

QUARTZ AND OTHER SAND-SIZED PARTICLES

CALCIUM CARBONATE ($CaCO_3$) CEMENTS THE SANDS TOGETHER

"The calcium carbonate might be dissolving," said Dr. Glassman gravely. "And when that happens, the sand particles fall apart."

At the end of the meeting, the general consensus was that Sam Dorey and his boatyard were the villains.

The next day Barry and Brent were walking toward the obelisk, fishing rods over their shoulders. Jeb Brown was propped up against the memorial as always. "Hi, Jeb," said Brent. "How about showing me that great fisherman's knot you told me about?"

As Jeb worked over Brent's pole, Barry turned his back to the boatyard and fingered the obelisk's deeply cut words on the north side. Then he walked to the side that faced west. The afternoon sun covered its surface with a red glow as he read the wording there:

IN HONOR
OF THE
FEARLESS
WHO SERVED
THEIR NATION
AND
DEFENDED
THEIR
LOVED ONES

"These letters are so sharply carved," said Barry. "Wonder how they did it then."

Jeb snorted. "It's how they do it *now* that's goina' be important. 'Cause it's goina' have to be done over, the rate my grandfather's name's disappearing. Look over here on this side." He twisted around to the worn south side. Then he moved some of the white grit on the ground around with his shoe. "From the boatyard's sandblasting," he stated.

As they left, Jeb called to them: "Now don't you boys go out too far in that dinghy of yours. A spring shower could be on its way, makin' it tough to find the harbor again."

"Oh, thanks, Jeb. We always stay close to shore. And anyway, it'd be hard to get lost with that huge 300-meter-high smokestack as a landmark."

Jeb agreed. "Yep, might be 'hundred miles south of us, but you can see it like it's next door."

At the boatyard, Sam Dorey was just finishing sandblasting a boat's hull. Compressed air shot small dark particles out of a nozzle, and as the sand grains hit the wood, the sailboat's peeling paint vanished.

Barry and Brent were walking toward the docks as Sam removed the cardboard protecting the boat's windshield. "I only burn wood and paper," he said to no one in particular as he threw the folded cardboard into his incinerator. "No way that my smoke's eating into sandstone. No, sir."

Barry didn't catch any fish that day. Which was understandable because, as Brent told his father later that night, "He never even baited his hook! He just sat there, looking like his brain weighed a ton."

"Well, I had a lot on my mind, Dad," Barry answered his father's unspoken question. "It's the Town Hall and the memorial problem," he said as he turned to his brother. "Brent, something just isn't interfacing."

Brent squinted at Barry, then asked solemnly, "And do you have a theory, supported by facts, of course?"

Barry's slow smile looked confident. "Clues are stacking up."

Barry put
the pieces together.
CAN YOU?

While Jeb Brown showed Brent how to tie a knot, Barry had rubbed his fingers over the north and west sides of the obelisk. And he noticed that the words were not worn away but were sharply cut into the sandstone. It was only the *south* side of the memorial—where Jeb loved to sit and catch the morning sun on his face—that was dissolving.

But the boatyard was in the wrong place to cause damage to the obelisk's south side. Another clue was the sand at the foot of the monument. It was white, unlike the grit used at the boatyard. When Barry considered these facts, he was sure that Mr. Dorey was not to blame for the problem.

The prevailing wind was from the south. Barry thought this fact was the key.

Barry asked his father about the huge smoke-stack down the coastline. Mr. Bytes said it belonged to a smelter—an industrial plant where rocks were heated until the metals they contained were melted and separated out. Then they could be collected.

But Barry knew that metal isn't the only product of smelting. Gases, released when the rocks are heated, float into the air and mix with dew, snow, and raindrops. The combination of the gas with the moisture makes acid rain.

Dr. Bytes suggested calling the smelter's acid rain monitoring station. Barry found out that the smelter's acid rain levels would dissolve sandstone at a rate of two millimeters a year.

Armed with that information, the Bytes boys created a program:

```
1000 REM SANDSTONE PROGRAM
1010 PRINT "ACID RAIN DISSOLVES 2 MM. OF"
1020 PRINT "SANDSTONE YEARLY."
1030 LET R=2
1040 PRINT "ENTER YEARS NEW STACK USED"
1050 INPUT Y
1060 LET H=R*Y
1070 PRINT "ACID RAIN DISSOLVED ";H;" MM."
1080 END
```

Before running it, they checked to make sure it would do what they wanted it to:

- -

1000 REM SANDSTONE PROGRAM
REM statements help the Byteses read their own programs. Computers ignore REM [for *RE-Mark*] statements. Each line of a program must have a number, like 1000, so the computer can keep track of the different lines. These numbers usually increase by tens, so you can change the program by adding lines [like 1005] in between.

. . . . .

1010 PRINT "ACID RAIN DISSOLVES 2 MM. OF"
1020 PRINT "SANDSTONE YEARLY."
A PRINT command tells the computer to print whatever is sandwiched between the quotation marks.

. . . . .

1030 LET R=2
Barry was told that 2 millimeters of sandstone would dissolve each year. This information became part of the program. R stands for rate. The word LET is not needed by most computers; programmers find it helpful. Some computers will not accept LET.

. . . . .

1040 PRINT "ENTER YEARS NEW STACK USED"
1050 INPUT Y

A taller stack was constructed one-and-a-half years before. The INPUT line will allow the computer to place that 1.5 in its memory until it is needed, in line 1060.

.....

1060 LET H=R*Y

Here the computer is asked to set aside a space in the computer's memory, a "memory box," called H. When R is multiplied by Y, the answer will be placed in that box. This H box is a variable container, because any number can be placed in it, like 5. Then the H would equal 5. The speed, or rate, at which sandstone dissolves [R, or 2] will be multiplied by the number of years [Y, or 1.5] the acid rain was affecting Lamont Landing. The * means multiply. So line 1060 is really telling the computer how to go about finding the answer, or H.

.....

1070 PRINT "ACID RAIN DISSOLVED ";H;" MM."

Here is where the computer will give the answer to the equation in line 1060.

.....

1080 END
END lets the computer know that the program
is completed. Some computers do not need this
line; others will not accept it.

-- -- -- -- -- -- -- -- -- -- -- -- -- -- -- -- -- --

When Brent and Barry finished debugging the
program, they ran it on Nibble, the computer between their beds:

```
ACID RAIN DISSOLVES 2 MM. OF
SANDSTONE YEARLY.
ENTER YEARS NEW STACK USED
?  1.5
ACID RAIN DISSOLVED  3  MM.
```

Once they had Nibble's computation, the
brothers headed for the obelisk. As Jeb fussed
around them, they held thread across the monument's flat surface. Then they used a tiny metal
millimeter ruler to measure the depth of the JEB
BROWN letters, as well as the lettering on the
side of the obelisk away from the wind.

If the acid rain were from the smelter, 3 millimeters should be worn away from the south
side, according to Nibble. It turned out that Jeb's
ancestor's name was 3 millimeters deep; the lettering on the side protected from the smelter
was 6 millimeters.

Strangely, the smelter had been ordered to build the superhigh stack because neighboring communities were practically drowning in acid rain. But with the new smokestack, the acid rain was carried higher in the sky, then traveled farther. So it then became a problem for communities hundreds of miles away.

Dr. Bytes presented her sons' findings at the next community meeting. Although the smelter was installing scrubbers that remove the acid-rain-making chemicals, it was decided to coat Town Hall and the obelisk with a special invisible substance that acid rain doesn't penetrate, while waiting to see if the scrubbers solved the problem.

People were still complaining about Sam Dorey's gritty sandblasting operation. Barry Bytes stood up and quietly suggested that Mr. Dorey sandblast only when the wind was blowing out to sea. This was such an obvious solution that the room grew silent for a few seconds. Then Sam Dorey announced that he had purchased an emission-control system for his incinerator.

Old Jeb Brown was back sunning himself early one morning, leaning beneath his grandfather's name. It was nice to know, he contentedly said to himself, that this memorial to his ancestor would be there long after Jeb wasn't. Particularly now that Sam Dorey had sand-blasted the carved letters to their original depth.

Just then the sea gulls flew overhead. Jeb stood up and headed for his morning cup of coffee, and for the newly coated Town Hall.

2
Shadows

Dr. Bytes hugged her sweater close to her. "Brrr," she said as she opened the front door, "even the idea of going out for the mail gives me the shivers."

It was the first blustery day of fall. Brent knelt by the hearth, balling up paper and arranging kindling, while Barry, waiting for the roaring flames, sprawled on the carpeting reading a mystery. Mr. Bytes stepped over him while balancing an armful of wood.

"Mark," Dr. Bytes spoke to her husband as she shuffled through the mail, "that letter you were waiting for, from the ski resort in Utah? Here it is."

"Are we going skiing?" Brent sat up straight, bumping his head on the top of the fireplace.

"That's not a bad idea, *if* my proposal is accepted," answered his father as he tore open the envelope.

The letter would tell Mr. Bytes, a computer consultant, that the Powderpuff Ski Center wanted him to design a computerized system capable of handling everything from the flow of skiers in lift lines to the number of bendable straws needed in the restaurant.

"Anyone for popping popcorn?" asked Brent as he headed for the kitchen.

At the same time the Byteses were munching buttered popcorn and planning their trip to Utah, a lone skier was smoothly carving down one of Powderpuff Mountain's snow-covered expert slopes.

Suddenly the skier was hit by a tremendous force. It took a few seconds for her to realize that another skier—dressed completely in black, including a face mask—had plowed into her.

"I'm terribly sorry. I didn't see you through the snow. Here, let me help you up. Are you hurt?" The black-clad man was concerned.

With his help the woman got herself upright. "No, I'm fine," she answered as she stepped into her bindings. "Just a bit shaken." She smiled to reassure him.

One hour later, the woman walked into the base lodge for a hot cup of mocha with whipped cream. It wasn't until she reached into her pocket that she realized that all her money was gone.

It was exactly three days after the on-slope pickpocketing that the four Byteses were in a lift line, anxious to start the first downhill run of their vacation.

Brent and his mother rode the double chairlift together. At the top, as they stood to ski off the lift, Brent's left tip crossed Dr. Bytes's ski. Mother and son ended in a tangled mass of skis and poles. The lift operator stopped the chair to give them time to get out of the way before the next two skiers had to get off.

The next pair happened to be Mr. Bytes and Barry. "Holy macro," said Barry, stopping next to Brent, who was slipping his pole straps back onto his wrists. "How do you do it?"

His annoyed brother didn't answer. Instead he turned to his mother, who was dusting snow off her pants legs, and said with dignity, "Mom, why don't you go ahead? That way I won't have to wait for you."

Dr. Bytes was diplomatic enough to remain silent. In a flash she was gone. Her family leaned on their ski poles as they watched her red parka disappear into the falling powdery snow.

After Barry and his father took off in the opposite direction—down a run designated More Difficult—Brent followed the path his mother had taken.

He made easy, relaxed turns. The snowfall was light; it was a beautiful day. There was no wind on the silent mountain. The temperature was mild. He noticed the graceful aspen trees lining the packed snow-covered ski run as he searched downslope for his mother.

Brent thought he spotted her as he approached a difficult mogul. He planted his pole on the crest of the bump, then skied around its side.

Finally, he thought, I'm getting my ski legs back.

He looked below again. No, it wasn't his mother after all. Whoever it was had fallen—Dr. Bytes, an expert skier, rarely did that—and appeared to be wearing red and black. Her outfit was all red.

But as he got closer, he realized it was his mother after all, assisted by a person in black.

Brent skied up just as the man swiftly took off down the slope.

"Wow," said Dr. Bytes breathlessly, "that guy really knocked me for a loop. He must have been traveling awfully fast." She looked downhill. The man was gone. "Funny that he should run into me on an empty slope. He's obviously an excellent skier, hard to imagine him so out of control."

"Now, Dr. Bytes," said the police chief apologetically, "please go over your story one last time. Exactly when did you discover that your money was missing?" Dr. Bytes nodded from her chair in the ski area's main office.

While she talked, Powderpuff's manager turned to Mr. Bytes. "Mark, I'm terribly sorry about this. This is the fourth incidence of pickpocketing we've had in the last three weeks." He pointed to a calendar hanging over his desk. Brent and Barry saw that the earlier robberies were circled in black.

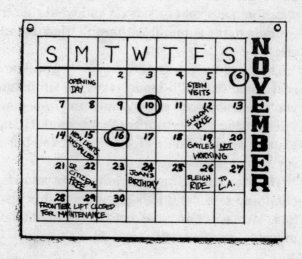

"And Jill here"—he gestured toward Dr. Bytes—"is the first one to give us a decent description of the thief."

She shook her head. "I don't know how much good it'll do since I can't tell you what his face looked like."

The police chief looked tough. "Six of my officers are getting on their skis. And we've already got eleven ski patrol people out there searching the mountain. Within two hours, I'll have our man."

Barry and Brent followed their parents outside to the rack where they'd left their skis and poles, next to the cumulative snowfall chart. Mr. Bytes said heartily: "Can't let this thing ruin our vacation. Let's get our skis on and we'll ride the gondola to the summit. We haven't tried that run yet."

The boys were less enthusiastic. "You know, Dad," said Brent, "it kinda' takes the wind outa' you when someone steals something from you."

His father's cheerful expression died. He put his arm around Brent. "I know what you mean, son."

Then he turned to the cumulative snowfall chart and said, "But look at the snow this place has. We've got to take advantage of it. Let's move!"

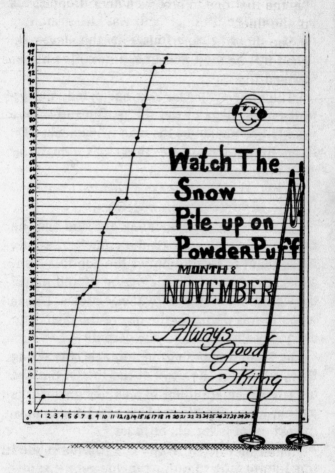

Of the six skiing policemen, one twisted his ankle on his first run and another dropped his pole from the lift chair and was still searching for it. The remaining four, plus the eleven ski patrollers, located and questioned five black-clad men.

Of the five suspects, four had skied Powderpuff on the days of the thefts. But only three were tall enough to be the man who knocked Dr. Bytes down. One of the three was a beginner skier and was eliminated.

Dr. Bytes could not make a positive identification between the remaining two.

One of the two suspect skiers said that he couldn't have committed the crimes. The only place he ever skied—under the gondola—enabled him to practice slaloming in and out of the strong shadows cast by the gondolas. This is what he was doing on the day of the thefts and every day that he skied Powderpuff.

The second man had no alibi. He was skiing Powderpuff on the days of the thefts. But the only thing he admitted to was being sorry his mother had given him a black parka and matching ski overalls for his birthday.

"Dad," said Brent when his parents related this information to him, "can you get me snowfall precipitation reports for the pickpocketing days from the computer?" Before Mr. Bytes

could answer, Brent had his parka on and was heading for the door.

"Where're you off to, son?" asked his father.

"Be right back," Brent called over his shoulder. "I want to recheck the cumulative snowfall chart."

"What's up?" asked Barry as he caught up with his fast-moving brother.

"That gondola slalomer is a liar. And I bet I'll be able to prove it," he said as he began to lay out his idea for Barry.

Later, when he had the precipitation report in hand, he and Barry agreed that the best way to present his case to the police was in the form of a graph. "More graphic," stated Brent.

NOVEMBER

Climatological Data/
Daily Precipitation Report

UTAH

TEMPERATURE AND PRECIPITATION EXTREMES

HIGHEST TEMPERATURE:	DEWEY
LOWEST TEMPERATURE:	WOODRUFF
GREATEST TOTAL PRECIPITATION:	BRYCE CANYON N.P. 1 S
LEAST TOTAL PRECIPITATION:	WENDOVER AUTOB
GREATEST 1 DAY PRECIPITATION:	BRYCE CANYON N.P. 1 S
GREATEST TOTAL SNOWFALL:	SILVER LAKE
GREATEST DEPTH OF SNOW OR ICE:	BLOWHARD MIN. RADAR

SNOWFALL AND SNOW ON GROUND

Station		1	2	3	4	5	6	7	8	9	10	11	12	13	14	15	16	17	18	19	20
North Central 03																					
Corinne	Snowfall										2	2.4	5								
Eureka	Snowfall										4	1	3	6							
Farmington usu flo sta	Snowfall										3		5	2.3							
Johnson Pass	Snowfall										2.5	3									
Logan 5 exp farm	Snowfall											2.8	1	3.1							
Powderpuff Mount	Snowfall	4				14	13	1	2	1	14	5	4		11	6	9	10		3	
Scofield	Snowfall		1.1									7	1.7	1.3	0.2						
Brighton	Snowfall			0.5							3	12	11	9	1						
											2	2	1	2						0.5	
											2.5		3	2					3	1	
													2.3								
																7	5	5	4	4	
																				5	

They set to work using Powderpuff's micro-computer:

```
1000 PRINT "SNOWFALL PROGRAM"
1010 PRINT
1020 PRINT "HOW MANY DAYS DO YOU"
1030 PRINT "WISH TO GRAPH?"
1040 INPUT N
1050 DIM D(N)
1060 DIM S(N)
1070 FOR I=1 TO N
1080 PRINT
1090 PRINT "ENTER DATE"
1100 INPUT D(I)
1110 PRINT "ENTER SNOWFALL"
1120 INPUT S(I)
1130 NEXT I
1140 PRINT
1150 PRINT "INCHES"
1160 PRINT "
1170 PRINT "     0     5     0     5"
1180 FOR J=1 TO N
1190 PRINT D(J);
1200 IF D(J)<10 THEN 1220
1210 GOTO 1230
1220 PRINT " ";
1230 IF S(J)=0 THEN 1270
1240 FOR K=1 TO S(J)
1250 PRINT "X";
1260 NEXT K
1270 PRINT
1280 NEXT J
1290 END
```

Handwritten annotations:
- SKIP 13 SPACES (pointing to line 1140 area)
- SKIP 3 SPACES (pointing to line 1150)
- SKIP 4 SPACES (pointing to "1   1"" at line 1170)
- "1   1"" (handwritten after line 1160)
- SKIP 4 SPACES (pointing to line 1190 area)

The debugging went quickly after Barry pointed out that the snow had stopped and the sun was shining. It was a perfect day to hit the slopes.

– –

1010 PRINT
When Powderpuff's computer sees just the PRINT command, it skips a line in the run.

. . . . .

1020 PRINT "HOW MANY DAYS DO YOU"
1030 PRINT "WISH TO GRAPH?"
Because these words follow the PRINT instruction and are within quotation marks, they will show up in the run, asking the boys how many days of precipitation data they wish to input.

. . . . .

1040 INPUT N
Here is where Brent and Barry will input the data asked for in lines 1020 and 1030. This line assigns a value to N and sets up an N memory box [see page 14, line 1060].

. . . . .

1050 DIM D(N)
1060 DIM S(N)

DIM allows data to be placed in an array, or table of columns and rows. In the run, D will be replaced by a date of the month. A number will also replace S—the inches of snowfall on that date. This replacement of D and S will repeat N times [see line 1040]. The D numbers will form an up-and-down column, and the S data will be across, in rows.

•••••

1070 FOR I=1 TO N

Here the computer is instructed to loop—rerun the same set of lines over and over. It will loop through the lines below this command until it reaches the command NEXT, which is at line 1130. The loop will be repeated N times [see line 1040].

•••••

1080 PRINT

See in the run how each request for data is separated by a blank line. This PRINT statement instructs the computer to print a blank line.

•••••

```
1090 PRINT "ENTER DATE"
1100 INPUT D(I)
1110 PRINT "ENTER SNOWFALL"
1120 INPUT S(I)
```

This code has the computer request the dates of the month, then the amount of precipitation, or snow, on each of those dates. The loop, begun at line 1070 and ending at 1130, was set up so these data could be asked for over and over, until all the dates and number of inches of snowfall are in the computer's memory.

NOTE: *For some computers, replace 1100 and 1120 with:*

```
  1100 INPUT D
  1105 D(I)=D
  1120 INPUT S
  1125 S(I)=S
```

For computers that do not automatically roll up, or scroll, add:

```
  1128 CLS
```

.....

1130 NEXT I
The loop ends.
NOTE: *Some computers need line 1135 @%=0 to make the numbers of the graph line up correctly [see line 1190].*

.....

1140 PRINT

Just the word PRINT causes a line to be skipped so the graph will not run into the printed lines above it.

. . . . .

1150 PRINT "INCHES"
1160 PRINT "   1   1"
1170 PRINT "   0   5   0   5"

These lines print INCHES and the numbers for the inches in the graph: 0, 5, 10, 15. The $\frac{1}{0}$ stands for ten; the $\frac{1}{5}$ stands for fifteen.

. . . . .

1180 FOR J=1 TO N

Here the loop begins that will print the graph.

. . . . .

1190 PRINT D(J);

D(J) causes the dates to print along the side of the graph. The semicolon makes a space after each date so the first X of each bar will line up under the proper number for inches of snow.
NOTE: *If, in the run, the X's don't line up properly alongside the dates, try adding " " ; after the ; . [Skip two spaces between those quote*

34

marks.] If the dates are printed too far to the right, add a ; after the word PRINT.

$\cdots\cdots$

```
1200 IF D(J)<10 THEN 1220
1210 GOTO 1230
1220 PRINT " ";
```

If the date is earlier in the month than the tenth [10], the computer must skip an extra space [see line 1220] for the bar graph to line up.

NOTE: Some computers require a GOTO after the THEN [lines 1200 and 1230]; others will not accept a GOTO.

$\cdots\cdots$

```
1230 IF S(J)=0 THEN 1270
1240 FOR K=1 TO S(J)
1250 PRINT "X";
1260 NEXT K
```

This code starts the loop that prints the bars, or X's, in the graph. The more snow, the greater the number of X's.

$\cdots\cdots$

```
1270 PRINT
```

A line must be blank between each bar.

$\cdots\cdots$

1280 NEXT J
The loop which began at 1180 ends here.

— —

Both Mr. Bytes and Powderpuff's manager
watched as the program was run.

```
SNOWFALL PROGRAM

HOW MANY DAYS DO YOU
WISH TO GRAPH?
?  19

ENTER DATE
?  1
ENTER SNOWFALL
?  4

ENTER DATE
?  2
ENTER SNOWFALL
?  0

ENTER DATE
?  3
ENTER SNOWFALL
?  0

ENTER DATE
?  4
ENTER SNOWFALL
?  0
```

```
ENTER DATE
?  5
ENTER SNOWFALL
?  14

ENTER DATE
?  6
ENTER SNOWFALL
?  13

ENTER DATE
?  7
ENTER SNOWFALL
?  1

ENTER DATE
?  8
ENTER SNOWFALL
?  2

ENTER DATE
?  9
ENTER SNOWFALL
?  1

ENTER DATE
?  10
ENTER SNOWFALL
?  14

ENTER DATE
?  11
ENTER SNOWFALL
?  5
```

```
ENTER DATE
?  12
ENTER SNOWFALL
?  4

ENTER DATE
?  13
ENTER SNOWFALL
?  0

ENTER DATE
?  14
ENTER SNOWFALL
?  11

ENTER DATE
?  15
ENTER SNOWFALL
?  6

ENTER DATE
?  16
ENTER SNOWFALL
?  9

ENTER DATE
?  17
ENTER SNOWFALL
?  10

ENTER DATE
?  18
ENTER SNOWFALL
?  0
```

```
ENTER DATE
?  19
ENTER SNOWFALL
?  3

INCHES
                1    1
    0    5      0    5

 1  XXXX
 2
 3
 4
 5  XXXXXXXXXXXXX
 6  XXXXXXXXXXXX
 7  X
 8  XX
 9  X
10  XXXXXXXXXXXXX
11  XXXX
12  XXXX
13
14  XXXXXXXXXXX
15  XXXXXX
16  XXXXXXXXX
17  XXXXXXXXX
18
19  XXX
```

The trail was no longer cold.
DO YOU SEE WHY?

By studying the cumulative snowfall chart, Brent noticed that there seemed to be a great deal of snowfall on the days of the crimes. Once he got the daily precipitation reports, he was sure.

His graph made a picture that the authorities couldn't ignore.

The dates that the skier—his name was Joe Digit—claimed to be under the gondola's shadows were also days that it snowed. This was the perfect time for him to ram into people, claiming visibility was poor.

It was not a day to slalom around gondola shadows, for when the sky is obliterated by falling snow, there is no sunlight to make shadows.

Once the villain was taken to jail, Powderpuff Ski Center's manager told the boys they could stay and ski for as long as they wished. Dr. Bytes firmly said they could ski until the day school vacation ended, as planned.

"Well, Brent, you did a fine bit of work," his father said on their last evening in Utah, over a delicious barbecue dinner.

"Yep," added Barry. "And that Joe Digit tried to pull a real snow job."

The Byteses grimaced over their ears of corn.

3

Bank Robber

On the flight home from Utah, the plane was packed. Barry settled into his window seat, popped a pillow behind his head, and pulled out his mystery. Before the plane was above the clouds, he was lost in a world of gloved safe-crackers and a fat detective with his hat brim worn low.

Suddenly the aroma of food and Barry's nose connected. He looked up. The flight attendants had begun to serve a meal at the front of the cabin.

The heavyset man seated next to Barry was sniffing the air too. As trays were placed in front of them, the man unfolded his napkin, surveyed Barry's tan, and grinned. "Been skiing, I bet! Hah?"

And so it happened that, by the time the flight attendants were collecting lunch trays, the smiling stranger knew all about the shadowy story of the slaloming sneak thief, including its computer conclusion.

"That's fascinating, Barry. Now I've got one for you. Maybe you can turn it into another keyboard caper. Haw-haw." The man looked pleased with this touch of levity as he pressed a button and his seat reclined.

Then his tone became more businesslike, and the wrinkles on his huge, jolly face ironed out. "I'm a special kind of investigator, hired by insurance companies to solve crimes that affect them." He smiled in spite of himself as he added, "Usually in the pocketbook.

"Fifteen years ago a bank was robbed. The thief absconded with one million dollars." His eyes became O's, silently conveying to Barry that this was an impressive amount.

Barry answered the man's expression with, "Holy macro."

The man's cartoonlike head nodded, his earlobes flapping. He continued his tale: "To everyone's surprise, the perpetrator entered the police station the following morning and surrendered. He admitted robbing the bank but said he couldn't remember what he did with the money!" The insurance investigator's incredulous face conveyed what *he* thought of the thief's story.

"The judge, who thought he was lying, gave him a harsh sentence—fifteen years.

"The bank had insurance for such losses, as banks are required to. The insurance company had to replace the million dollars. They hired me to investigate the crime and to try to recover the cash from the robber.

"I visited the ex-con the day he was released from prison—that was yesterday—and told him that I would trail him forever." The investigator's Play-Doh face collapsed into what would be a serious expression on a bulldog. "He'd never be able to enjoy the money because, I warned him, I'd be watching all the time."

Now the investigator looked like he was bursting to deliver a great punch line. He controlled himself for dramatic effect and took a giant slurp of his drink. The ice cubes jiggled. The straw made a big gurgle in the bottom of the cup.

Barry sensed that the story's climax was near as the unusual face rearranged itself into an I-know-something-you-don't expression. Barry stared, fascinated, as the large, rubbery mouth slowly opened and words came out, one at a time. "Can —you—guess—what—happened?"

The man's eyes twinkled as a massive grin tightened the loose skin hanging all over the face. Barry was by now deep in thought and didn't even notice. Finally he looked up and said, "Yes, I think I can. . . . I'll bet he handed you the million dollars, didn't he?"

"Wh-at? How did you know?" The wrinkles had quickly returned but almost instantaneously disappeared into a laugh. "Haw-haw. I guess you made a lucky guess, Barry, because what that criminal did makes no sense at all. The only thing I can figure is that he really did forget what he did with the money, then remembered while in prison."

Barry considered the possibility. "I don't think so. But what I really need to do is to get home so I can work this out on my computer. I'd be happy to send you a printout."

"Mail it? No sir. Just tell me where you live, and what time to pick it up. I like the idea of a floppy disk frenzy—haw-haw."

Barry was right on the money. ARE YOU?

Barry bet that the crook placed the million dollars in a bank account. So, before he went to work with Nibble, he found out what rate of interest bank accounts were paying fifteen years before.

Then he devised a program to show how much money a million dollars would earn in fifteen years:

```
1000 PRINT "BANK ROBBER PROGRAM"
1010 PRINT "PRINCIPAL"
1020 INPUT P
1030 PRINT "ANNUAL INTEREST"
1040 INPUT I
1050 I=I/100
1060 PRINT "NUMBER OF YEARS"
1070 INPUT Y
1080 FOR J=1 TO Y
1090 D=P*I
1100 P=P+D
1110 NEXT J
1120 PRINT "AFTER ";Y;" YEARS"
1130 PRINT "THE TOTAL AMOUNT IS $";P
1140 END
```

Before he ran the program, he studied it carefully. He didn't want to give the insurance investigator a program with bugs in it:

— —

1000 PRINT "BANK ROBBER PROGRAM"
There must be quotation marks around the words in this PRINT statement. Some computers save their programmers time by accepting a ? instead of the word PRINT.

· · · · ·

1010 PRINT "PRINCIPAL"
1020 INPUT P
The principal is the amount of money that is deposited. It is this cash that will earn more money, which is called interest. In the run when the computer asks for the amount of principal, Barry will type in $1 million this way: 1000000.

· · · · ·

```
1030 PRINT "ANNUAL INTEREST"
1040 INPUT I
1050 I=I/100
```

Banks pay customers a certain percentage in interest on the money that they deposit in an account. If you were to place $100 in a bank that paid 8% interest each year, or annually, then you would earn $8 during that year, as payment for leaving your cash in the bank [so *the bank* can invest it, at a higher rate of interest. This is how banks make money]. Barry found out that the interest paid fifteen years before, when the thief deposited his $1,000,000, was 6%. This means that for every $100 left in the account, $6 would be earned at the end of one year. In line 1050, the interest, which will be 6 in this run, is divided by 100. This places the decimal point in the correct position in the answer.

NOTE: *Some computers require LET at the beginning of lines 1050, 1090, and 1100. A few will not accept it.*

· · · · ·

```
1060 PRINT "NUMBER OF YEARS"
1070 INPUT Y
```

In the run, Nibble will need to know how many years the cash was in the bank earning interest. Y will equal the number of years.

· · · · ·

```
1080 FOR J=1 TO Y
1090 D=P*I
1100 P=P+D
1110 NEXT J
```

Here is a FOR . . . NEXT loop. This is where Nibble will calculate the interest. In the first year, $1,000,000 will earn $60,000, if the bank is paying 6% annual interest. To arrive at this answer, you would multiply 6%, or .06, which is the same thing, times 1,000,000 [one million dollars]. This $60,000 interest money is now also in the bank and earning interest during the second year. At 6% a year, $1,060,000 will earn $63,600. So . . . in the third year, there will be $1,123,600 earning interest! The FOR . . . NEXT loop is necessary, for Nibble will have to repeat the calculations we just did, again and again for Y times, which in the bank robber's case will be 15, for 15 years. What Nibble is doing is called compounding interest—the interest earned from each year is added to the principal and earns interest as well. If Y were a large number, Barry would see Nibble slowing down, as the amounts of money became bigger and more cumbersome to calculate.

· · · · ·

```
1120 PRINT "AFTER ";Y;" YEARS"
1130 PRINT "THE TOTAL AMOUNT IS $";P
```
Nibble will print the answer at these lines. The spacing around the Y keeps the answer from "jamming up" against the words.

- -

This is what the program-run looked like:

```
BANK ROBBER PROGRAM
PRINCIPAL
?  1000000
ANNUAL INTEREST
?  6
NUMBER OF YEARS
?  15
AFTER  15  YEARS
THE TOTAL AMOUNT IS $ 2396558.19
```

"A clever trick," said Barry to the investigator when he came by to see the run. "He had to spend a lot of time in prison, but he sure got paid for it—one million, three hundred ninety-six thousand, five hundred fifty-eight dollars and nineteen cents' worth, after subtracting the original million dollars he returned to you. And a person can't be tried twice for the same offense, so no one can do anything about it."

"Haw-haw! That's where you—and he—are wrong!" The investigator cheerfully explained that, during the time the bank robber was in jail, a law was enacted making it illegal to benefit from the proceeds of a crime.

The criminal was sued by the insurance company for the proceeds—the interest earned—on the million dollars. The insurance company, which already had the million dollars, now recovered the interest paid on that money over the fifteen-year period.

As Barry put it, "I guess we now know the true meaning of 'Crime doesn't pay.' Haw-haw!"

4

Bingo!

"Got much more to do?" twelve-year-old Elana Lynsky asked her neighbor Brent Bytes, who was wiping the microwave oven.

"Two more chores and we'll get to work." Brent and Elana were going to generate a random-number program for the Lamont Landing bingo games to be held three Saturdays in a row.

He grabbed the cleanser and attacked the sink.

Elana picked up a rag and headed for the stairs. "While you're finishing your work, I'll dust Dribble."

Brent exhaled, dragonlike, through his teeth. Elana insisted on calling the Bytes boys' computer by the wrong name. It peeved Brent so much that he never noticed that she spent as much time as possible with the terminal.

When he finished wiping the banister, Brent walked into the room he shared with Barry. Elana was typing at the keyboard. "Oh-h," she stuttered,

"I was just cleaning the keys." On the monitor's screen were four lines of a program:

```
1   READA,B:FORX=ATOB:READY:POKEX,Y:NEXTX
2   DATA826,849,162,128,160,0,132,33,134,34,177, 33,73,128,145,33,200,200,247
3   DATA232,224,132,208,240,96,0
4   SYS826
```

Brent began to look it over. "Interesting." He paused for a minute. "But what is it?"

"Oh, let me get rid of that. It's just something like machine language I'm fooling around with and don't really know what I'm doing." She cleared the screen in a flash, then changed the subject. "Ready to tackle the bingo program?"

"Move over!" Brent was raring to go. "I've got a code in my node."

"Better have some tea with honey and lemon," said Dr. Bytes, passing the room. "If you catch these things right at the beginning . . ."

Brent, staring hard enough at the monitor to vaporize the phosphorus coating, didn't hear. "This is a toughie," he said, editing a line for the third time.

"What about flowcharting it first?" suggested Elana.

"Huh? What?" He surfaced for a minute. "Great thinking, for someone who is only semi-computer literate."

For someone not yet computer literate, Elana

made an astonishing number of suggestions and corrections.

"Now wait a minute," said Brent as he looked over the result. "Why do we have that there?"

"Come on," she said, "get your binary logic in gear and we'll go over each step":

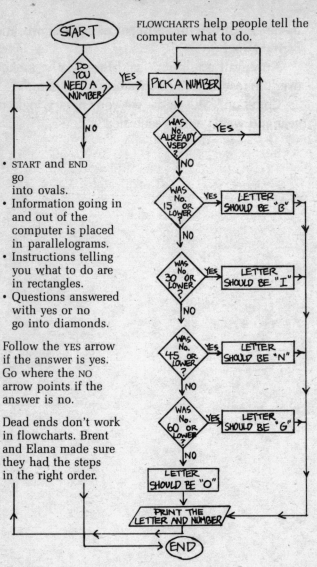

FLOWCHARTS help people tell the computer what to do.

- START and END go into ovals.
- Information going in and out of the computer is placed in parallelograms.
- Instructions telling you what to do are in rectangles.
- Questions answered with yes or no go into diamonds.

Follow the YES arrow if the answer is yes. Go where the NO arrow points if the answer is no.

Dead ends don't work in flowcharts. Brent and Elana made sure they had the steps in the right order.

62

"Now," said Brent, satisfied with their work, "for the program":

```
1000 PRINT "BINGO PROGRAM"
1010 DIM F$(75)
1020 PRINT "DO YOU NEED A NUMBER (Y OR N)"
1030 INPUT A$
1040 IF A$="N" THEN 1230
1050 N=INT(75*RND(9)+1)
1060 IF F$(N)="USED" THEN 1050
1070 F$(N)="USED"
1080 IF N<=15 THEN 1140
1090 IF N<=30 THEN 1160
1100 IF N<=45 THEN 1180
1110 IF N<=60 THEN 1200
1120 L$="O"
1130 GOTO 1210
1140 L$="B"
1150 GOTO 1210
1160 L$="I"
1170 GOTO 1210
1180 L$="N"
1190 GOTO 1210
1200 L$="G"
1210 PRINT L$ ; " " ; N
1220 GOTO 1020
1230 END
```

NOTE: Add LET and GOTO if required by the computer. A few computers will not accept, and do not need, line 1010. Others need these additional lines after 1000:

```
1001 DIM A$(1)
1002 DIM L$(1)
```

and some need the following change to know that no more than four characters will be read:

```
1010 DIM F$(75,4)
```

Certain computers which do not automatically scroll need:

```
1035 CLS
```

Machines using string emulation require the following changes:

```
1010 DIM F(75)
1060 IF F(N)=999 THEN 1050
1070 F(N)=999
```

[999 is a "dummy" value; any number would work here.]

Computers vary in the way they generate random numbers. If necessary, try each of these in place of line 1050:

```
1050 N=RND(75)
```

or:

```
1050 N=INT(RND(1)*75)+1
```

or:

```
1050 LET N=INT(RND*75)+1
```

Some need an extra line:

```
1005 RANDOMIZE
```

"Let's try it," said Elana. Brent dug a couple of bingo cards out of a drawer and was shaking his piggy bank for pennies as Elana loaded the program:

```
BINGO PROGRAM
DO YOU NEED A NUMBER (Y OR N)
? Y
I  19
DO YOU NEED A NUMBER (Y OR N)
? Y
I  23
DO YOU NEED A NUMBER (Y OR N)
? Y
I  24
DO YOU NEED A NUMBER (Y OR N)
? Y
N  39
DO YOU NEED A NUMBER (Y OR N)
? Y
B  5
```

```
DO YOU NEED A NUMBER (Y OR N)
? Y
G  60
DO YOU NEED A NUMBER (Y OR N)
? Y
N  38
DO YOU NEED A NUMBER (Y OR N)
? Y
I  28
DO YOU NEED A NUMBER (Y OR N)
? Y
O  74
DO YOU NEED A NUMBER (Y OR N)
? Y
O  68
DO YOU NEED A NUMBER (Y OR N)
? Y
G  55
DO YOU NEED A NUMBER (Y OR N)
? Y
B  1
DO YOU NEED A NUMBER (Y OR N)
? Y
O  73
DO YOU NEED A NUMBER (Y OR N)
? Y
O  72
DO YOU NEED A NUMBER (Y OR N)
? Y
B  4
DO YOU NEED A NUMBER (Y OR N)
? Y
G  50
DO YOU NEED A NUMBER (Y OR N)
? Y
N  42
```

```
DO YOU NEED A NUMBER (Y OR N)
? Y
O  62
DO YOU NEED A NUMBER (Y OR N)
? Y
O  69
DO YOU NEED A NUMBER (Y OR N)
? Y
O  65
DO YOU NEED A NUMBER (Y OR N)
? Y
O  66
DO YOU NEED A NUMBER (Y OR N)
? Y
N  44
DO YOU NEED A NUMBER (Y OR N)
? Y
N  34
DO YOU NEED A NUMBER (Y OR N)
? Y
B  3
DO YOU NEED A NUMBER (Y OR N)
? Y
G  46
DO YOU NEED A NUMBER (Y OR N)
? Y
G  59
DO YOU NEED A NUMBER (Y OR N)
? Y
I  22
DO YOU NEED A NUMBER (Y OR N)
? Y
B  11
DO YOU NEED A NUMBER (Y OR N)
? N
```

It was Saturday night. The hall was filled and the bingo program was running beautifully. Elana and Brent were having a grand time.

After the large final prize was won, Mr. Hall stood up and said a word to all who helped make the evening a success. Then he added, "And a special thanks to Brent Bytes and Elana Lynsky for the computer program." He wore a weak-tea smile. "I think it has probably helped a number of us adults keep our bytesophobia under control."

"Our *what*?" Brent's voice was a trifle loud. He wondered if he should be insulted.

"It means 'a fear of computers,'" said Elana in her adult tone.

"Hey, Bytes." A tall, scrawny boy tapped Brent's shoulder. "I'd like to see a list of your computer program. Could I?"

"Sure, Kip," said Brent, not sounding sure at all. "I could make you a printout tomorrow."

As Brent and Elana walked home, Elana asked, "Wasn't that the Kip you were telling me about who's a real keyboard abuser? How come you're being so generous?"

"Who knows, if I show him how to treat a computer system with respect, maybe he'll change his ways." They rounded the street corner before Brent added, "The question is, what's he want the bingo list for?"

The following Saturday night's bingo was just as much fun as the first. People were milling about during the refreshment break, waiting for the final game and the grand prize. A group of adults surrounded the computer; Kip, partially blocked from view by the onlookers, was seated at the keyboard.

A moment later Kip, Brent, and all the other players sat down, ready for the final game as Elana said, "I hope it's my turn to yell 'bingo!'" Neither she nor Brent had won yet.

The program was loaded. In no time Elana was one number away from bingo in two different directions:

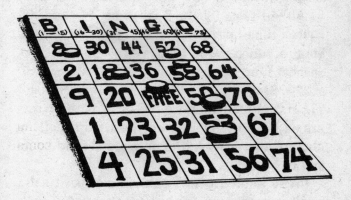

Mr. Hall asked the computer for another number. "O, seventy-f . . ."

Elana held her breath.

". . . ive."

"Bingo!" It was Kip, sitting a couple of rows behind Brent and Elana.

"Darn," said Elana. "How come he wins three times in a night and we don't win at all in two nights?"

Brent sighed. "Let's go. Maybe we'll have better luck next week."

They didn't. And it was particularly frustrating because, on the following Saturday, Kip won two more times.

"Impossible," Brent answered when Elana pointed this out.

"But it happened," she said firmly as they took their seats for the final game.

This time both Brent and Elana were on the verge of bingo as Mr. Hall's voice called out, "O, seventy-four. O, eighty-seve . . ."

". . . Bingo!" Actually, Kip explained as people surrounded him, he had won with O, seventy-four, but he was so tired from yelling "bingo" that it took him an extra second to respond.

Brent walked over and took a look at Kip's card:

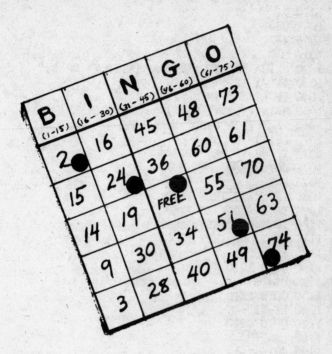

"Amazing," said Brent with a tired sigh.

Elana was staring straight ahead. "Not really," she declared as she stood up and headed for the computer.

"What is it?" Brent was following her.

She sat down and, on power up, asked for a list:

```
1000 PRINT "BINGO PROGRAM"
1010 DIM F$(75)
1015 CH=1
1016 X=2
1017 C=0
1020 PRINT "DO YOU NEED A NUMBER (Y OR N)"
1030 INPUT A$
1040 IF A$="N" THEN 1230
1050 N=INT(75*RND(9)+1)
1060 IF F$(N)="USED" THEN 1050
1070 F$(N)="USED"
1075 IF CH=1 THEN 1078
1076 GOTO 1080
1078 N=X
1080 IF N<=15 THEN 1140
1090 IF N<=30 THEN 1160
1100 IF N<=45 THEN 1180
1110 IF N<=60 THEN 1200
1120 L$="O"
1130 GOTO 1210
1140 L$="B"
1150 GOTO 1210
1160 L$="I"
1170 GOTO 1210
1180 L$="N"
1190 GOTO 1210
1200 L$="G"
1210 PRINT L$ ; " " ; N
1215 C=C+1
1216 X=X+3+C
1220 GOTO 1020
1230 END
```

"Ew, boy," she said, warming to the task as she looked over the output. Then she asked for a run:

```
BINGO PROGRAM
DO YOU NEED A NUMBER (Y OR N)
 ?Y
B  2
DO YOU NEED A NUMBER (Y OR N)
 ?Y
B  6
DO YOU NEED A NUMBER (Y OR N)
 ?Y
B  11
DO YOU NEED A NUMBER (Y OR N)
 ?Y
I  17
DO YOU NEED A NUMBER (Y OR N)
 ?Y
I  24
DO YOU NEED A NUMBER (Y OR N)
 ?Y
N  32
DO YOU NEED A NUMBER (Y OR N)
 ?Y
N  41
DO YOU NEED A NUMBER (Y OR N)
 ?Y
G  51
DO YOU NEED A NUMBER (Y OR N)
 ?Y
O 62
DO YOU NEED A NUMBER (Y OR N)
 ?Y
O  74
DO YOU NEED A NUMBER (Y OR N)
 ?Y
O  87
DO YOU NEED A NUMBER (Y OR N)
 ?N
```

Bingo! Elana figured out what was happening. HAVE YOU?

When Mr. Hall began to call "O, eighty-seven," Elana knew that the program had been tampered with. That number is out of the range of the numbers on a bingo card, where each column has fifteen available numbers to choose from (this information is listed at the top of each column on the card):

—The B column includes one through fifteen.
—The I column includes sixteen through thirty.
—The N column includes thirty-one through forty-five.
—The G column includes forty-six through sixty.
—The O column includes sixty-one through seventy-five.

She and Brent sat down and studied the list. It was like their original program except for the lines with line numbers not ending in zero. These had been added by Kip:

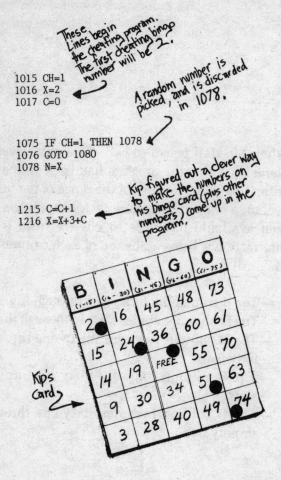

These Lines begin the cheating program. The first cheating bingo number will be 2.

```
1015 CH=1
1016 X=2
1017 C=0
```

A random number is picked, and is discarded in 1078.

```
1075 IF CH=1 THEN 1078
1076 GOTO 1080
1078 N=X
```

Kip figured out a clever way to make the numbers on his bingo card (plus other numbers) come up in the program.

```
1215 C=C+1
1216 X=X+3+C
```

Kip's Card →

B (1-15)	I (16-30)	N (31-45)	G (46-60)	O (61-75)
2	16	45	48	73
15	24	36	60	61
14	19	FREE	55	70
9	30	34	56	63
3	28	40	49	74

Kip, the only other person with knowledge of the original program, had sat down at the keyboard during the refreshment intermission and changed the bingo program.

When the bingo winner's sneaky deed was exposed, the keyboard abuser quickly became a loser.

Bingo!

5

Sea Gulls

Old Jeb Brown was in his usual spot at the obelisk, enjoying the late afternoon summer sun, when the flapping of dozens of wings made him look up.

A wedge of sea gulls was traveling inland, cawing as they went. Okay, my friends, he told them silently, you don't have to shout; I know it's time to head for the Fishmonger's Café for my coffee and pie. Jeb always said he didn't need a watch; the gulls kept time for him.

As Jeb walked away, Luke Gardner called from behind. "Ho, Jeb, not so fast." Luke also had his afternoon break at the 'Monger, but was usually scraping his dessert plate as Jeb arrived.

"Why so late?" Jeb asked.

"I had a miserable job to finish. Troublesome sea gulls got into the garbage again, and Mr. Hadley had me pick up every little piece before I could knock off work." His expression suggested that Luke would be pleased to have southern fried gull for dinner.

Jeb, who considered the great gray, black, and white birds his own personal property, was unsympathetic. "Come on, Luke, don't knock the gulls. I think they're great. Say, did you hear about the new bird scientist—they call him an or-nee-thologist, I think—who's studying our gulls? Seems they're different from sea gulls in other places in the way they follow such a crazy schedule, coming and going at the exact same time."

Luke nodded as he looked over the 'Monger's daily specials.

"Crazy thing about those gulls," Jeb said.

"Mom," Barry Bytes spoke to his mother's back as she rinsed strawberries at the kitchen sink. "What is there to make for a brown-bag lunch? Pearl and I are going bike riding to the lighthouse."

"Well," began Dr. Bytes, "there's the leftover . . ."

Just then there was a knock.

"Hi, Pearl." Barry opened the screen door for his friend. "I just have to get my lunch together and then we can leave."

"That's what you think," said Pearl, pointing

to where the garbage pails were kept, by the back door. It was a mess. "I bet it was a raccoon."

Dr. Bytes walked over and took a look as a couple of gulls landed in the middle of the yard and began fighting over a bread crust. She pursed her lips. "You'd better get that picked up, Barry, or they'll spread it all over the grass." And back she went to her colander full of strawberries.

"Yuk," said Barry, as he got to work.

Dr. Bytes waited to hand Barry a paper bag while he washed and dried his hands. "Thanks, Bar, you were a good sport. Here's your lunch, packed with special goodies. Enjoy."

She stood outside and watched Barry wheel his bike out of the garage. "Oh, Bar, you and Pearl might want to stop by my lab on the way back." Dr. Bytes, a marine biologist, worked at the Marine Laboratory. "I've got a visitor from Australia who's writing a gull-migration program."

"Sounds neat, Dr. Bytes. We will," answered Pearl.

As they rode, Pearl, a bit of a computer-language linguist, called out, "I wonder what language the Aussie is writing his program in."

"My guess is FORTRAN—stands for 'FORmula TRANslation,'" Barry yelled back. "Scientists like it because it contains plenty of mathematical functions."

It was late afternoon when they parked their bikes in the rack alongside the Marine Lab. At the sound of cawing, Pearl looked up. "Must be four-thirty. Here come the gulls."

Barry shaded his eyes with his hand and looked toward the sky. "Are they really as on time as everyone says?"

His question was answered a few minutes later in his mother's lab. Dr. Outback, a marine ornithologist from the Australian city of Sydney, was seated in front of a keypunch machine, with a pile of continuous-roll paper falling off his lap.

"These gulls you have," he said to Barry and Pearl after Dr. Bytes had introduced everyone, "are truly amazing. I'm just punching the data I collected yesterday onto these cards. Once the computer reads and plots the data, I think we'll see an unusual pattern."

He leaned back, sticking out his lower lip in thought. "Your local gulls appear to travel in straight lines, which is unusual. Not only that, they also follow a strange schedule which might have to do with the angle of the sun, or even magnetic fields." The scientist explained that magnetite—a magnetic mineral—had been found in the brains of bees and pigeons. "And we think this helps them navigate. Might be true for gulls too."

"How did you collect these data?" asked Barry, tapping one of the cards.

The ornithologist explained that huge nets were shot out of a cannon. "About one hundred birds are collected in a cannon net. Then we record information about the bird—sex and so on, put a numbered band on its leg for future identification purposes, then attach a transmitter around its chest."

"Goodness, you mean you're tuned in to hundreds of birds flying around?" Pearl was astonished.

"Dr. Outback," said Barry glancing at Pearl, "we'd be interested in helping you the next time you do a study." Pearl nodded enthusiastically.

Dr. Outback looked pleased. "Then meet me here at six o'clock tomorrow morning. And be prepared to be in the field until five in the evening. Then we'll come back here and keypunch our data onto cards."

The following day was long, exhausting, and exciting. After netting the birds and attaching the transmitters, Barry and Dr. Outback climbed into a mobile unit. Pearl teamed up with a graduate student named Robin who was studying the gulls as part of her training.

In each truck was a radio receiver. The vehicles traveled up and down the coast, staying in radio contact with the gulls' transmitters. Every fifteen minutes the teams recorded the direction each gull was heading—called the bearing, or azimuth—and the distance the bird had traveled.

At the end of the day, the four workers took their data to the Lab where they punched it onto computer cards:

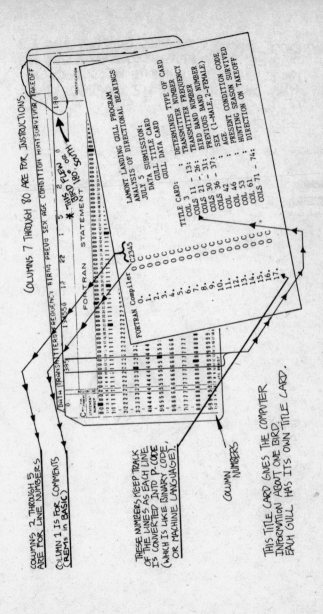

COLUMNS 7 THROUGH 80 ARE FOR INSTRUCTIONS

COLUMNS 2 THROUGH 5 ARE FOR LINE NUMBERS

COLUMN 1 IS FOR COMMENTS (REMS IN BASIC)

THESE NUMBERS KEEP TRACK OF THE LINES AS EACH LINE IS CONVERTED INTO P-CODE (WHICH IS LIKE BINARY CODE, OR MACHINE LANGUAGE).

COLUMN NUMBERS

THIS TITLE CARD GIVES THE COMPUTER INFORMATION ABOUT ONE BIRD. EACH GULL HAS ITS OWN TITLE CARD.

* THIS BIRD FLEW 0 180° SOUTH

LAMONT LANDING GULL PROGRAM
ANALYSIS OF DIRECTIONAL BEARINGS
JULY 5   DATA SUBMISSION:
                 GULL TITLE CARD
                 GULL DATA CARD

TITLE CARD:
  COL 3   : : DETERMINES TYPE OF CARD
  COLS 11 - 13:   TRANSMITTER FREQUENCY
  COLS 21 - 26:   TRANSMITTER NUMBER
  COLS 30 - 31:   BIRD BAND NUMBER
  COLS 36 - 37:   PREVIOUS BAND NUMBER
  COL 42   :   SEX (1-MALE, 2-FEMALE)
  COL 46   :   AGE
  COL 53   :   PRESENT CONDITION CODE
  COL 61   :   HUNTING SEASON SURVIVED
  COLS 71 - 74:   DIRECTION ON TAKEOFF

EVERY 15 MINUTES, THE GULL'S DIRECTION AND ITS DISTANCE TRAVELED WAS RECORDED. A CARD WAS MADE FOR EVERY 15-MINUTE PERIOD. HERE ARE FOUR CARDS FOR BIRD #12, WHO HAD A TOTAL OF 18 CARDS.

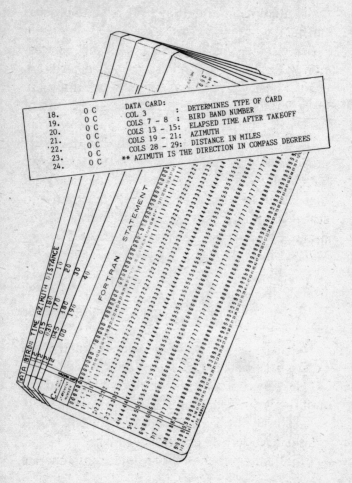

		DATA CARD:	
18.	0 C	COL 3 :	DETERMINES TYPE OF CARD
19.	0 C	COLS 7 – 8 :	BIRD BAND NUMBER
20.	0 C	COLS 13 – 15:	ELAPSED TIME AFTER TAKEOFF
21.	0 C	COLS 19 – 21:	AZIMUTH
22.	0 C C	COLS 28 – 29:	DISTANCE IN MILES
23.	0 C C	** AZIMUTH IS THE DIRECTION IN COMPASS DEGREES	
24.	0 C		

While they were working, Pearl mentioned that punched cards were first used in the late 1700s in France, "right after the French Revolution. And computer cards became popular in the United States after they were used to process census data for the year 1890."

Barry looked at her with his "huh?" expression as Robin mentioned that punched cards are used less and less "because tape and disks are more efficient ways to input large amounts of data."

Dr. Outback had written a four-hundred-line program that would make sense out of the gull data. "You can look at the program, Pearl, on that terminal over there." Pearl sat down and scanned about one hundred lines before feeling dizzy. She rubbed her eyes. "I think I've got VODS."

"Vods?" asked Barry as he took her place in front of the monitor.

"Video Operator's Distress Syndrome. Makes you gweepy."

Dr. Outback wrinkled his nose. Gweepy? the Australian repeated to himself.

"Holy macro," effused Barry, from behind the monitor. "Some program!"

"Well, it does what we want. In BASIC, it would have to be a great deal longer."

Finally the punched cards, including separate

ones punched with the program, were placed in a box and delivered to the computer room. The staff there would run them during the night—mainframe computers are usually up twenty-four hours a day—and the processed data would be waiting for Dr. Outback in the morning.

Barry and Pearl planned to be there too but overslept. By the time they arrived, Dr. Outback had analyzed the printout, then had drawn a map of the gulls' flight patterns:

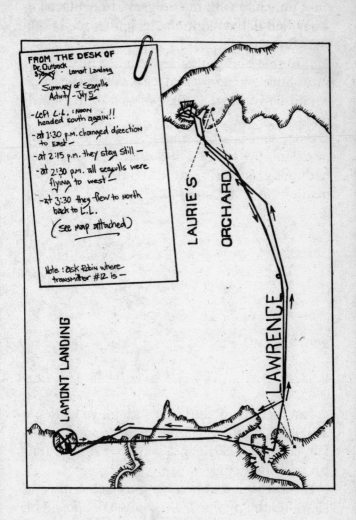

FROM THE DESK OF
Dr. Outback
Sydney — Lamont Landing

Summary of Seagulls
Activity — July 5

- Left L.L. : NOON
  headed south again!!

- at 1:30 p.m. changed direction
  to East —

- at 2:15 p.m. they stay still —

- at 2:30 p.m. all seagulls were
  flying to west —

- at 3:30 they flew to NORTH
  back to L.L.

  (see map attached)

Note: ask Robin where
transmitter #12 is —

LAURIE'S

ORCHARD

LAWRENCE

LAMONT LANDING

"Now let me show you," said Dr. Outback as he pulled out another chart, "typical gull flight patterns."

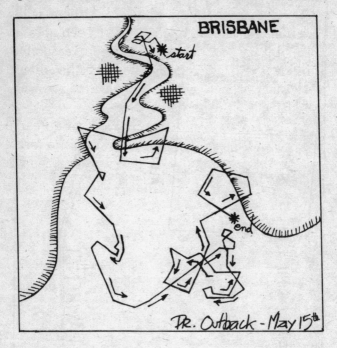

Just then the phone rang. "It's for you," Robin said to Dr. Outback. "The Lawrence and Laurie's Orchard Ferry System, about your reservations for this afternoon."

Dr. Outback grabbed his ferry schedule and said into the phone, "Okay, now I'm booked on the 1:30 ferry in the afternoon. What time did you say I return? The next day at . . . ? Oh, 2:30. . . ." as Barry and Pearl quietly discussed the diagrams.

Dr. Outback hung up and said to them as he too glanced at the papers, "We've been able to pinpoint the birds' schedule. But the reason behind it is still unclear." He smiled as he added, "All suggestions from young hackers are welcome," and he winked at Robin.

"I'm glad to hear you say that," said Pearl, straightening up as Barry picked up the ferry schedule and route map, "because Barry and I have solved your mystery."

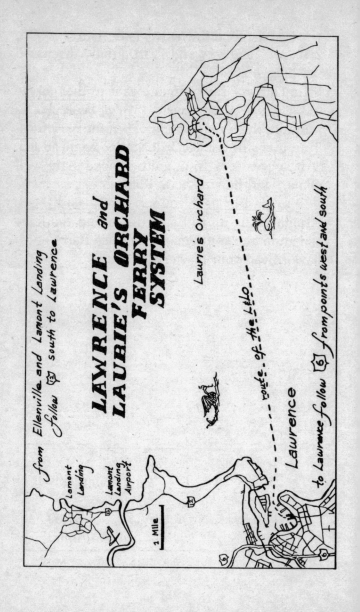

LAWRENCE and
LAUBIE'S ORCHARD
FERRY
SYSTEM

Laurie's Orchard

Lawrence

route of the ferry

From Ellenville and Lamont Landing
follow 🛣 south to Lawrence.

Lamont
Landing

Lamont
Landing
Airport

1 Mile

to Lawrence follow 🛣 from points west and south

LAWRENCE/LAURIE'S ORCHARD

SUMMER SCHEDULE
Effective: <u>June 15</u> thru <u>Sept. 14</u>

FROM LAWRENCE TO LAURIE'S ORCHARD	DEPART	DUE	TRIP
	1:30 pm	2:10 pm	A
	3:30 pm	4:10 pm	C
	5:30 pm	6:10 pm	E

FROM LAURIE'S ORCHARD TO LAWRENCE	DEPART	DUE	TRIP
	2:30 pm	3:20 pm	B
	4:30 pm	5:20 pm	D
	6:30 pm	7:20 pm	F

PASSENGER FARES

Between Lawrence and Laurie's Orchard	Oct 15– May 14	May 15– Oct. 14
Adult one way	$3.50	$4.00
Child (5–15) one way	$1.75	$2.00

BICYCLE FARES

	One Way
Between Lawrence and Laurie's Orchard	$1.00 additional

RATES AND SCHEDULES SUBJECT TO CHANGE WITHOUT NOTICE

Pearl and Barry had a bird's-eye view of the problem.
DO YOU?

"In this case," Barry began to explain, "the evidence is a lot of garbage." He held up his palm as both Robin and Dr. Outback opened their mouths to speak, and explained the first clue: gulls fighting over garbage in the Byteses' backyard a couple of days before.

Pearl continued. "Then we overheard you making a ferry reservation. And . . ."—she paused for dramatic effect—". . . the ferry departure times coincided with the birds' schedule."

"Now why," asked Barry with a glint in his glasses, "would the gulls' comings and goings be the same as the ferry schedule?"

"Beauty, mate!" Dr. Outback looked excited. "Why didn't I think of that?"

"Of what?" Robin was still in the dark.

Dr. Outback turned to her. "The gulls follow the ferry for the leftover food that the boats dump at sea."

Robin snapped her fingers. "And for the handouts. The tourists are always offering the birds potato chips."

"But," said Dr. Outback, looking puzzled, "I don't understand." He picked up his note and pointed to the fifteen minutes between 2:15 and 2:30. "They seem to stay in one spot for a while; then they suddenly take off and retrace their tracks."

"Oh," said Pearl, examining her nails, "that's when they wait in Laurie's Orchard for the ferry's return trip to Lawrence."

"Ahhh . . ." said Robin.

She, Pearl, and Dr. Outback were comparing the ferry route map with Dr. Outback's note as Barry announced in a serious tone: "I suppose we can safely report"—a smile slipped out—"to the world's ornithologists that our Lamont Landing sea gulls are out to lunch."

The Bytes Brothers
Micro-Dictionary

ARRAY   When data are organized in a
               series of rows and columns, an
               ARRAY has been created.

BASIC   The most commonly used
               microcomputer language is
               BASIC, which stands for *BE-
               GINNER'S ALL-PURPOSE
               SYMBOLIC INSTRUCTION
               CODE*. Its language includes
               commands like FOR ... NEXT
               and GOTO.

BINARY   A number system with only
               two numerics: "0" and "1."

BYTE   A set of eight bits—On/Off
               switches—is called a BYTE.

BYTESOPHOBIA   A fear of computers and computer information.

CHARACTER   A mark or symbol. A forty-character monitor has space for forty letters, numbers, spaces, or symbols.

CODE   A set of rules that must be followed to use information in computers. A computer program is written in code.

COLUMNS   A vertical—up and down—arrangement of print. (See ARRAY and ROWS.)

COMPUTER   A machine with a memory, made up of bytes. A COMPUTER can make decisions and can handle both words and numbers; a calculator cannot. And unlike a calculator, a COMPUTER can be programmed to do the same thing over and over. (See LOOP.)

DATA   Facts a computer processes.

You feed DATA into a computer and get information from it.

DEBUG　　　　　To identify, find, and correct errors in a computer program.

DELETE　　　　　To remove or erase.

DIM　　　　　A program instruction that stands for *DIMENSION*. It sets up a table of columns and rows within the computer's memory.

END　　　　　The last line of a program, which tells the computer not to search for more program lines.

EQUATION　　　An EQUATION compares two different but equal sets of terms.

FLOWCHART　　A step-by-step way to plan a program with paper and pencil, charting the steps needed to solve a problem using a computer program.

FOR . . . NEXT — This computer statement begins a loop, which will repeat itself any number of times it is programmed to.

FORTRAN — An acronym for *FORMULA TRANSLATION*, this programming language solves mathematical and scientific problems, such as sea gull flight-pattern questions. FORTRAN was the first widely used high-level (close to English) programming language.

FUNCTION — A computer performs a required action, or FUNCTION.

GENERATE — To create, to produce, or to form.

GOTO — GOTO tells the computer to move on to a certain line.

HOME COMPUTER — Also called a micro or personal computer, it is designed for individuals rather than institutions or businesses.

IF . . . THEN   A programming statement in which IF something is true, THEN the computer gets special instructions; if it is false, the computer drops to the next line.

INPUT   Data fed into a computer by humans or by other computers. In a program, INPUT causes a ? or other prompt to appear on the monitor during the run, and tells the computer to wait for a response. (See PROMPT.)

INTERFACE   The communication between different computer devices.

KEYBOARD   A typewriterlike device, usually with special computer-function keys added, used to input data into a computer.

KEYPUNCH   A machine invented in the early 1900s by an American named Herman Hollerith to tally census statistics. The KEYPUNCH machine records data by punching rectangular holes in stiff cards in a pattern that the computer can read. Each punched hole stands for the binary "1." (See BINARY.)

LET

This is a programming term not required by most computers. It helps humans remember that the value of a variable can change. LET A = 5 means: Allow A to take the place of 5. Later in the program this might be changed, and A might, for example, stand for 12 or G.

LIST

The actual program, or set of instructions to the computer, is called a LIST. To bring a program up (to see it on the monitor), the programmer keyboards LIST.

LOAD

This statement asks the computer to locate a particular program on the disk, tape, etc., so it can be listed, run, or debugged. (See LIST, RUN, and DEBUG.)

LOOP
A computer action that keeps repeating itself. (See FOR . . . NEXT.)

MACHINE LANGUAGE
Computer languages—BASIC, APL, Pascal, FORTRAN, Logo, and others—are converted into this totally numeric language which the computer understands.

MACRO
A set of instructions given to a computer. MACRO is also a computer language.

MAINFRAME
A large computer with many capabilities, used by governments, corporations, banks, and hospitals. Different groups can take turns, or time-share, on the same MAINFRAME.

PERCENTAGE
A portion or share of 100 is called a PERCENTAGE (%).

109

PRINT
All characters that follow PRINT in a program and are surrounded by quotation marks will be printed.

PRINTOUT
One of the methods a computer has to communicate. A PRINTOUT is letters and numbers on paper.

PROGRAM
A set of logical step-by-step instructions given to a computer in language it can understand.

PROMPT
The computer displays a ? or other PROMPT, then waits for data input. (See INPUT.)

RANDOM NUMBER
A RANDOM NUMBER is a number that is as likely to occur as any other. Computers generate RANDOM NUMBERS using the BASIC random function.

REM
REM is short for **REM**ARK. In the run, computers ignore REMs. When a computer program says REM, it is going to

make a remark or give information rather than take an actual step in solving a problem.

ROWS — A horizontal—sideways—arrangement of print. (See ARRAY and COLUMNS.)

RUN — This command starts a program.

SYNTAX ERROR — A mistake in the computer language, such as a misspelled BASIC word.

VARIABLE — A character or a group of characters, like C or A(I,J), in a program that stands for a value that can vary, or change, during a run.

VODS — An acronym for *VIDEO OPERATOR'S DISTRESS SYNDROME*. Prolonged activity with computers can cause dizziness, nausea, headaches, and an unhappy outlook, or VODS.

ABOUT THE AUTHORS

LOIS AND FLOYD MCCOY, a wife-and-husband team, create the Bytes Brothers mysteries and write the programs. Lois McCoy is a journalist and author with a scientific background. Floyd McCoy conducts research on oceanography and volcanology at Columbia University. Dr. and Mrs. McCoy have four children, aged twenty-five, twenty-three, fourteen, and thirteen. They live in New York State, in a converted barn, and spend their summers in the scientific village of Woods Hole, Cape Cod.

Life, Love and Adventure from the Teenagers View

Here are books of life, love, adventure, mystery, and suspense for every teenager's interest.

CHOOSE YOUR OWN ADVENTURE ®

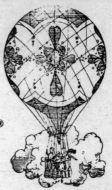

"You'll want all the books in the exciting Choose Your Own Adventure series. Each book takes you through dozens of fantasy adventures—under the sea, in a space colony, into the past—in which *you* are the main character. What happens next in the story depends on the choices *you* make, and *only you* can decide how the story ends!"

Prices and availability subject to change without notice.

Make sure you have all these great Interplanetary Spy books!

☐ 23506	**Find The Kirillian! #1** McEvoy, Hempel & Wheatley	$1.95
☐ 23507	**The Galactic Pirate #2** McEvoy, Hempel & Wheatley	$1.95
☐ 23700	**Robot World #3** McEvoy, Hempel & Wheatley	$1.95
☐ 23701	**Space Olympics #4** Martinez and Pierard	$1.95
☐ 23941	**Monsters of Doorna #5** McEvoy, Hempel & Wheatley	$1.95
☐ 23942	**The Star Crystal #6** Ron Martinez and Rich Larson	$1.95
☐ 24198	**Rebel Spy #7** Len Neufeld	$1.95
☐ 24521	**Mission To Microworld #8** Seth McEvoy	$1.95

Prices and availability subject to change without notice.

Buy these exciting Interplanetary Spy adventures wherever Bantam paperbacks are sold, or use this handy coupon for ordering:

Bantam Books, Inc., Dept. INS, 414 East Golf Road, Des Plaines, Ill. 60016

Please send me the books I have checked above. I am enclosing $_____ (please add $1.25 to cover postage and handling). Send check or money order —no cash or C.O.D.'s please.

Mr/Mrs/Miss _____

Address_____

City_____ State/Zip_____

INS—9/84

Please allow four to six weeks for delivery. This offer expires 3/85.

SPECIAL MONEY SAVING OFFER

Now you can have an up-to-date listing of Bantam's hundreds of titles plus take advantage of our unique and exciting bonus book offer. A special offer which gives you the opportunity to purchase a Bantam book for only 50¢. Here's how!

By ordering any five books at the regular price per order, you can also choose any other single book listed (up to a $4.95 value) for just 50¢. Some restrictions do apply, but for further details why not send for Bantam's listing of titles today!

Just send us your name and address plus 50¢ to defray the postage and handling costs.